Life Thru a Lens // Robbie Williams

Distributors:
Music Sales Limited
8/9 Frith Street,
London W1V 5TZ, England.
Music Sales Pty Limited
120 Rothschild Avenue
Rosebery, NSW 2018,
Australia.

Order No.AM953117
ISBN 0-7119-7082-3
This book © Copyright 1997 by Wise Publications
Visit the Internet Music Shop at
http://www.musicsales.co.uk

Music Sales' complete catalogue describes thousands of titles and is available in full colour
sections by subject, direct from Music Sales Limited. Please state your areas of interest and
send a cheque/postal order for £1.50 for postage to: Music Sales Limited, Newmarket Road,
Bury St. Edmunds, Suffolk IP33 3YB.

Wise Publications
London/New York/Sydney/Paris/Copenhagen/Madrid

Music Transcribed by Barnes Music Engraving Ltd., East Sussex TN22 4HA
Printed by The Panda Group · Haverhill · Suffolk CB9 8PR · UK
Binding by ABS · Cambridge

Art Direction, Intro
Photography, Andy Earl

Lazy Days

Words and Music by
Robert Williams and Guy Chambers

La - zy days
Cra - zy days

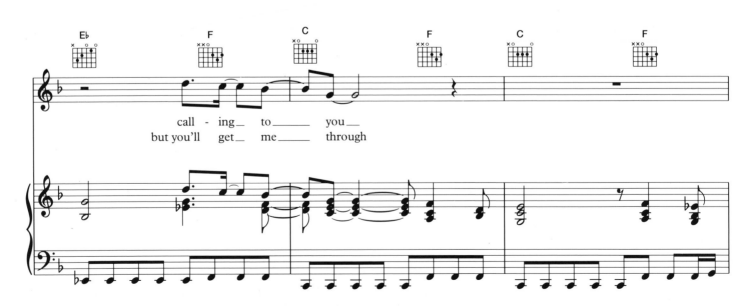

call - ing to_____ you_____
but you'll get_____ me_____ through

Life Thru a Lens

Words and Music by
Robert Williams and Guy Chambers

Ego A Go Go

Words and Music by
Robert Williams and Guy Chambers

Angels

Words and Music by
Robert Williams and Guy Chambers

South of the Border

Words and Music by
Robert Williams and Guy Chambers

Old Before I Die

Words and Music by
Robert Williams, Eric Bazilian,
and Desmond Child

She's tak-in' me plac - es I should ne - ver have been, ___
She's not feel-in' stab - le, she's un - ab - le to breathe,

she's show - in' me fac - es I should ne - ver have seen, ___
her heart's beat-ing fast - er so I'll ask ___ her to leave, ___

One of God's Better People

Words and Music by
Robert Williams and Guy Chambers

Let Me Entertain You

Words and Music by
Robert Williams and Guy Chambers

come on, come on, come on, come on, ___ come on, come on, come on, come on. ___

Let me en-ter-tain ___ you, let me en-ter-tain ___ you.

play 3 times and fade

Killing Me

Words and Music by
Robert Williams and Guy Chambers

Am
G♯aug
C/G
You paint my pic - ture black, the joke's on me and
I can't go on a - lone pre - tend - ing noth -
F♯m7♭5
Fmaj7
I don't wan - na laugh, re-mem-ber the good times,
- ing's wrong. May - be I just want
G
Fmaj7/A
1.
G/B
Esus4
won't you bring them back some - day, some-how.
to be-long some - day, some - how,
2.
G/B
E7sus4
A
Am7
some - how. Oh, oh, oh,

Clean

Words and Music by
Robert Williams, Antony Genn, Richard Hawley,
Martin Slattery and Pablo Cook

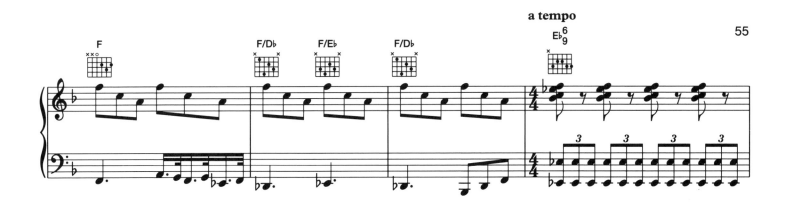

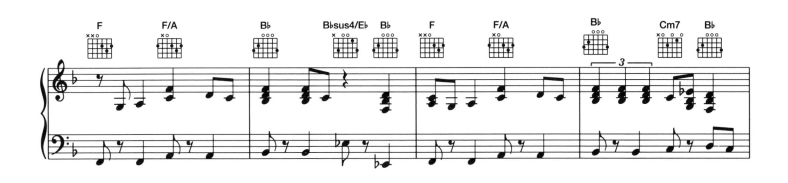

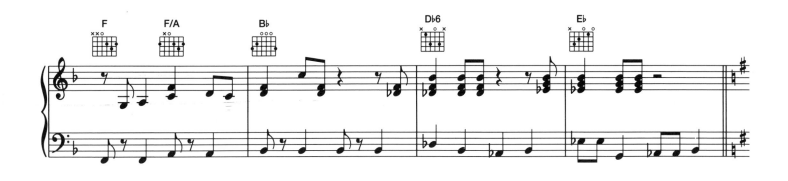

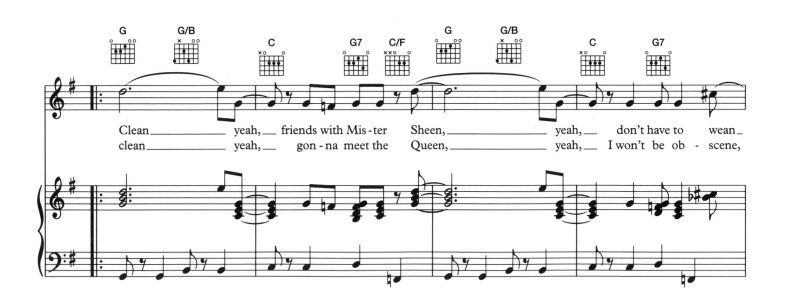

Clean _____ yeah, ___ friends with Mis - ter Sheen, _____ yeah, ___ don't have to wean_
clean _____ yeah, ___ gon - na meet the Queen, _____ yeah, ___ I won't be ob - scene,

Baby Girl Window

Words and Music by
Robert Williams and Guy Chambers

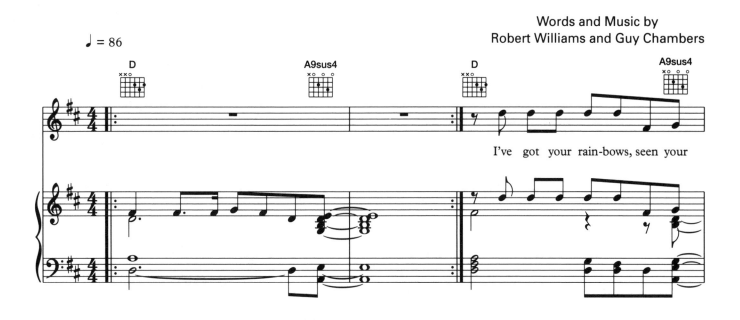

I've got your rain-bows, seen your

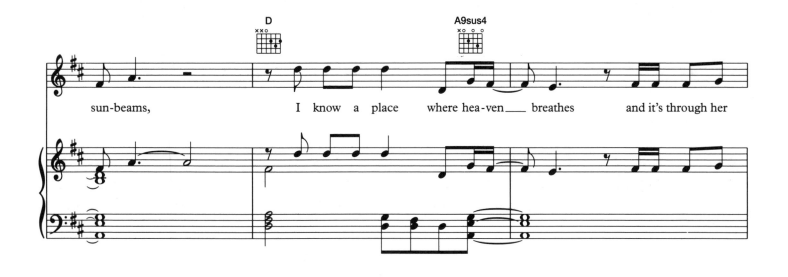

sun-beams, I know a place where hea-ven___ breathes and it's through her

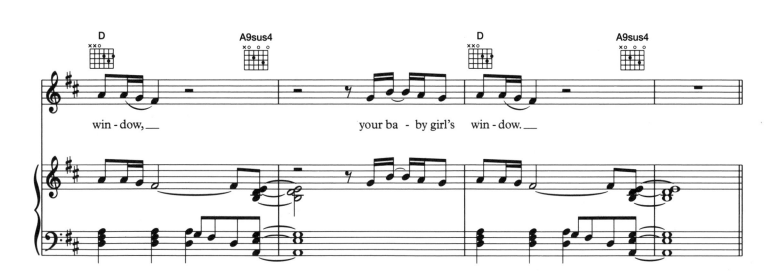

win-dow,___ your ba-by girl's win-dow.___

win-dow.

Ah _____ I wish you'd stay, ___

ah _____ to see what she made ___ of her-self. ___